MY VILLAGE IN IRELAND

Road to market

Road to kilmacduagh ↗

Road of the Dishes ↗

Blacksmith

The big store

KINVARA

Dun Guaire

The tailor

The Canon's house

Convent school and church

Where my cousins live and we play hurling

Willy Cara house

The we

Barley field

James Gaynor
lives here

Here the curragh
landed again

Meadow of
the Wise Men

Mick the Boat
lives here

School

Our
potato
field

St. Colman's
Church

Barley
field

Paddy lives
here

Seaweed banks

Here little Gerald
stood

A.M. JAUSS

SONIA and TIM GIDAL

My Village in Ireland

PANTHEON

My name is Patrick

My name is Patrick. Patrick Curtin it is, and everybody calls me Paddy. I was given my name in honor of St. Patrick. He is the great patron saint of our country.

I live in a village on the west coast of Ireland, in a cottage near the sea. One hundred yards of the shore belong to us, and everything we find there belongs to us, too: the seaweed for putting on the fields to make things grow better, and the carrageen moss for making pudding, and periwinkles for pocket money, and eels, and lobsters. But lobsters are rare.

Sometimes the high tide throws planks and bottles and strange objects up on the shore. They come from old shipwrecks out in the sea. I found an old Spanish coin on the shore in the spring. My father says the sea must have washed it up from far down below. Perhaps it came from one of those four-mast galleons that sailed in olden times from Spain to America. Even Columbus must have sailed right past our shore. He made for Galway Harbor as a last stop on his way to America, they say, and Galway city is only two hours away on my bicycle.

I often run down to the shore and look for things. I like running. I beat everybody in school at the hundred-yard dash, and Master Moylan gave me the medal for being the best runner. It is "Paddy the Runner" my schoolmates are calling me now.

Mother sewed the medal right on my corduroy jacket. "Paddy the Runner it is they call you?" she asked. And then she told me a strange story.

When the neighbors were visiting her the day after I was born into the world, it was Jenny McCarthy looked into the cradle and said: "Och, but he has only such skinny wee legs, and not strong they look for much walking." But Tom the castle-keeper, he answered: "Don't you say that, Jenny McCarthy!" And then he told what had happened to him this day.

There are blackthorn bushes along the wall of the castle. When he went by that morning, the mist was hanging low, and he kept a sharp lookout for the leprechauns, as is his custom. It is in such weather that those little goblins are bold and trust that they will not be seen. And sure enough, Tom said to my mother, there was one of the leprechauns sitting under a blackthorn bush, hammering away at a shoe as they always do.

Tom tried to catch him, of course, because the leprechauns give you anything you wish, just for letting them go. But they are very clever, and when Tom grabbed for the little fellow, he got only blackthorns in his hand, and did they hurt him!

Old Tom was ashamed, he was so sure of having seen one this time. He looked and looked, and he did not see the little goblin any more. But a four-leaf clover he found in the place where he thought he had seen a leprechaun before. "He gave it to me as a present, for bringing you good luck in life, Paddy," Mammy says, "and I remember well what he said then: Good luck and strong feet for little Patrick, and don't you be minding those words of old Jenny McCarthy!"

Where I live, there are seven cottages in the village. There are two other villages in our neighborhood, and all three villages belong to the same parish: we all go to the same church and the same school. Some houses stand far away from the villages, and the people there have to walk half a mile or even more to their next neighbor. And they all have a long walk to church and to school, which stand all by themselves on the road.

I am lucky, for we live only twenty minutes away from church, and half an hour's walk from school, and it is half an hour in the other direction to the well where we go with our donkey cart for fresh water every day.

I have four brothers and four sisters. Michael is my oldest brother, and Daddy and he and I, we whitewashed our cottage last week. We do it every year. This was fun, and when Daddy went into the cottage for another brush we whitewashed each other a bit, till Daddy came out and told us not to be so bold.

4

Michael and I climbed up on the thatched roof and painted the chimney white. Michael has done it before. He is already fourteen years old, and has finished school. But for me it was the first time, and Daddy held the ladder across the thatch, for creeping up on it. Gerald wanted to come up too, but he is only two years old. Johnny and Tommy had to carry him away from the ladder by force.

My sister Maureen is eighteen years old. She works in a grocery store in the city of Limerick. So now Bridie is the oldest girl around. She is seventeen. Then comes Teresa, who has brown hair, like Michael. Everybody else in my family has red hair and lots of freckles.

Little Carmel I do not see much, she is always hiding behind Mammy. She hides from our geese. Nobody knows why, but our geese like Carmel's fat little legs, and they go after them whenever they see her. Carmel hates the geese. But she loves our sheep—we have twenty. And of course she loves her pet lamb most.

5

Our donkey always throws me, but he never throws Johnny; that's just how he is, I can't do anything with him.

Bridie's and Michael's favorite is our horse, and they ride it any time they can. Tommy plays most with the goat, and he likes fighting her. Teresa and Bridie take care of the fourteen turkeys and our two cows and three calves, but I help feed them too. And Daddy looks after our twenty sheep and the horse, and all our many fields.

We have a big sow too. Twelve days ago she had ten pink little piggies. And then we have Captain, our Shetland dog. He is always around me, and we are friends.

All our fields are fenced in by stone walls, so the wind and the gales from the sea cannot bother the sheep, and cannot carry away the soil from the fields.

Where we live the wind is always blowing, because Ireland is an island and we do not have high mountains for keeping the winds away, I learned from Joe of the Pond. He knows all about the winds, Joe of the Pond does. He is the fisherman of the village.

The soft south wind is very good for the growing corn, he told me. The north wind is cold, and brings a bad harvest. The west wind is generous, it fills his nets with fish. But the east wind is an ill wind. The sky gets dark and gloomy, and the rain doesn't go away for days and days.

I know everybody for miles around. Mick the Boat lives farther up, on the shore. And Pete the Lorry lives far down the road, near the well. He takes our sheep and cattle to market in his big truck, and he brings the turf from the bogland for burning in the hearth.

Between our village and the Meadow of the Wise Men live the O'Malleys and then the O'Shaugnessys and the Cavanagh family and the O'Sullivan brothers. Nobody knows any more how the meadow got its name. Our schoolteacher, Master Moylan, said he would look it up, and perhaps he will find out about it from the old books.

Sunny day, and we are cuttin' the corn

I hear a knock at our door.

"There, it is half nine now, and no sign of you getting up!" That is Mammy's voice from the kitchen. I turn over in our bed. Michael and Johnny and Tommy are still sleeping. My sisters sleep in the next room. On the other side of the kitchen is my parents' bedroom. Little Carmel and Gerald sleep there too.

We put our brown corduroy suits on, and our sandals, and go in the kitchen for breakfast. Mammy's first words are:

"Go back and rack your hair!"

Every day the same words—and so we stand around the pail of water and dip our combs in, and comb and comb and comb!

When my hair looks all straight and shiny, Mammy sends me out with Tommy for feeding the calves. But outside the wind blows, of course, and my hair gets all messed up. I like that! Now I can comb it all over again.

Meanwhile Michael and Johnny go for milking the goat.

"It is a lovely day," Daddy says, as we leave the cottage. "Be quick with your work, lads, we will be cuttin' the corn today!"

So we are being fast, and walk to where the animals graze behind the stone fence. Johnny carries his blackthorn stick with him, and Tommy his hurling bat. He never lets go of that. He practices batting with pebbles, and he is really very good at it, though the bat is much too heavy for him.

7

We take a few stones from the fence, and step over it into the field. The calves come running up to me. I put the two buckets of fodder on the grass. They love the mixture of milk and meal and carrageen moss all cooked together. All three calves try to put their noses into the bucket at the same time. But this way nobody gets anything. I grab the bucket and push two calves away. Then I let the first calf feed. When I think it has enough, I let the second calf at the bucket, and then the third. I fill the buckets with water, and let the calves drink.

Michael is off milking the goat. She gives only one jug of milk a day, just enough for Gerald's breakfast. But she does not stand still, like our cows do. Johnny holds her fast by the ear, and he raises the blackthorn stick up in the air. While the goat watches the stick, Michael milks her.

On the far side of the field, Bridie and Teresa are milking the cows. They come over to us with their pails. We climb back over the fence, and put the stones back in place, and walk home for breakfast.

Mammy has let the hens and the turkeys out, and the rooster and the geese. They are cackling all over the place.

Now she carries a huge chunk of bacon from the pantry house. She took it from the wooden barrel in there, where it was kept for curing, salted down with coarse salt. And after that, it was covered for four weeks with straw to keep the air out. Mammy cuts thick cubes from the bacon, for boiling with cabbage for dinner.

After breakfast, Uncle Joe-John comes with his horse, and Daddy takes our horse, and they go to the barley field by the hazelnut bushes for cutting the corn. Uncle Joe-John and Daddy always help each other with their horses when either one of them needs two for going to the fields.

"Children, get potatoes home," says Daddy. "After that, come to the barley field for helping us with the sheaves. It's a sunny day, it looks as if we will have only a few short showers." Where we live we have many showers during the day, and we do not mind them. But when it rains hard for hours and days, we cannot harvest the corn, and it may even turn bad.

Our potato field is on the other side of the road, just across from our cottage. Bridie takes the rake, and Teresa holds a pail. Michael and Johnny and I disentangle the leaves, and then Bridie digs into the earth and brings up the potatoes. We shake the earth off them, and throw the potatoes into the pail.

When we dig in the potato fields, we often get to singing our potato song. Bridie starts off, and we join in:

> Work hand and foot,
> Work spade and hand
> Through the crumbly mould!
>
> The blessed fruit
> That grows at the root
> Is the real gold of Ireland!

"Look now," says Teresa, "Mother Superior is coming with Sister Margaret Mary."

Mother Superior stops and looks over the stone fence.

"Very sunny!" she calls her greeting, and we call back: "It is, it is, indeed it is!"

"Padraic, how are the potatoes coming along?" Mother Superior always calls me by my Irish name. And she calls Bridie Brigid, and with her she only talks in the Irish language, because Bridie went for many years to the convent school, where the Sisters taught her Irish. We all understand Irish, of course—the older children, I mean—because we learn it in school. But among ourselves and with the neighbors and at home, we speak English.

I walk over to the fence and show three fine potatoes. Mother Superior says: "It does make me happy when I see healthy potatoes, Padraic. You know why!"

11

Of course I know why. Everybody knows. It is because of the Great Famine over a hundred years ago, when the potato crop failed for three years. Over a million people died of starvation in the villages, and ever since those dreadful years, many more Irish people have emigrated to other countries. Before the Great Famine, eight million people lived on our island, but now we have only four million left. Even now, many people emigrate every year. But Daddy says we shouldn't always moan about the bad times, and I think Daddy is right. Daddy says there is enough room for everybody in Ireland, and everybody can make a nice living, and we should look ahead and be grateful for our good fields and fine crops now.

We carry the pails of potatoes home. Mammy washes a few handfuls of them in the big tub in the back yard. She puts them into the ten-gallon pot. "Hurry up now to the barley field," she says, "and you, Paddy, let the piggies out first!"

I open the door of the pigsty just a tiny bit and peep in. The ten little pink piggies stand close together in the corner and squeak and sniff the ground. I coax them to come out. Their mother scratches herself against the wall. I open the door wide, and now the piggies come running. They look so funny with their thin tails and long snouts.

I run after the others, down the lane, and turn left at the first crossroads. Everybody is busy binding the cut barley into sheaves.

"The weather will hold up," says Daddy. "I might be cuttin' all the corn today. The small showers will not bother us."

"It is a fine harvest this year," says Uncle Joe-John. "It is," answers Daddy. "Thirty barrels of malting barley I will be getting from these two acres, and twenty more barrels from my other two fields. With 250 pounds to the barrel, that will be 50 times 250 . . . that will be 125 and add two zeros . . . that will be . . . twelve thousand and five hundred pounds of barley!" Whoo—isn't it a mighty harvest we are having!

Daddy sells the malt barley to Mr. Guinness, who has a very big beer factory in Dublin city. He needs lots of barley for making beer.

We have forty acres of land, and we don't only grow barley and
potatoes! We grow turnips too, and cabbage and oats and lots of
sugar beets for selling to the factory, where they make sugar from
them. And then we have clover fields for green fodder and hay, and
grazing fields for our sheep.

Daddy reads his farming magazine every week, and he learns
from it new methods for getting even better crops, and keeping virus
and pests from the plants. Daddy loves to try out new methods.

"Come on, Paddy, don't stay there and be dreaming! Sit with me on
the machine!" Daddy calls to me. "We are cuttin' the rest of the field
now!"

I sit behind Daddy and work the brakes. The reaper cuts the
barley stalks. Daddy pulls the fallen stalks along with a long rake,

until a big heap collects. Then he raises the rake from the heap, lowers it again, and a new heap starts collecting.

Uncle Joe-John and Bridie and Michael and Teresa push the heaps together with their arms and bind them into sheaves.

Tommy and Johnny walk behind the others, and pick up the stalks that were left on the ground after the sheaves were made. "Every stalk counts," says Daddy.

"Why don't we always have barley in this field, Daddy?" I ask. "Last year we had beet roots, and before it was only grass."

"The earth is very kind to us, Paddy, and gives us really all we need. But we cannot go on for years and years taking the same kind of crop from the same field—that would weaken it too much. So every year we plant something different. We call it rotating the crops! And after three or four years we give the field a real rest. I just plough it in the fall, and next year only grass grows there, the emerald-green grass of Ireland, as we call it. It grows so well, because we have much rain, and it's the best fodder our sheep can get."

Daddy is in a good mood. He always is when he is cutting the corn. I think he likes it best of all the work he does. And going to market he likes. Tomorrow is market day, and I ask: "Will you be going to market tomorrow, Daddy?"

16

"I will. I'll be wanting to buy a few sheep, and your mother wants me to sell two turkeys and buy some pullets for the money I will be getting."

"I have never been to the market with you, Daddy."

"And wanting to come along you are, I know, lad. Michael is better for helping me there, he is older. But tomorrow you can come with me, I might as well be starting you off now."

"I am mighty glad, Daddy," I say.

The church bells ring the Angelus, it is twelve o'clock. We kneel down in the field and say our prayers.

We go home for dinner, and pass our sheep grazing in the field between the beet roots and the cabbage. Michael just drove them on to the field, and he has not yet put back the stones which he has taken from the fence for the sheep to go through. We always open and close our stone fences that way.

Daddy points to the sheep, and says to us: "I told Paddy this morning about rotating the crops. There you see it. On the left field I had corn last year, and this summer it is beets. In the middle field we had potatoes, and this year and next I let the sheep graze on it, so the earth gets back her strength; and then I will sow oats. On the right field the cabbage is coming up beautifully. Last year we had clover on it, for green fodder and hay."

"And the stone fences keep the wind away from the fields and from the sheep," says Teresa.

"That's right, Teresa. Johnny, would you know where all the stones come from for our fences?"

"No, I do not," Johnny says.

"Well, lad, they come from the fields. For hundreds of years every farmer took out the stones from the earth and put them on the road-side. Nowadays I rarely find a big stone in the fields, like the one we took out this morning. My forefathers have worked for me, as I work for you, and you work for your children. That's why we have good fences, and good fields!"

17

From the other side of the road I see Willy coming from his fields.

"Look, Daddy, Willy has a new horse today! The white one is Dolly, but he never worked with a brown one before. I do wonder whose it is!"

We wait on the road for Willy Cavanagh.

"Well, if it isn't Charlie he is using for work!" says Daddy, and he is surprised.

"Charlie! What would he be using his racehorse for working for, Daddy! Surely not Charlie!"

But the racehorse Charlie it is.

"Top of the morning to you," Willy Cavanagh greets us. But he does look upset.

"Very sunny it is," Daddy answers. "And do you not send Charlie to the races any more, that you let him work in the fields?" asks Daddy.

"Och, it is a sad story. Charlie tripped on the racing ring three weeks ago and fell. And he hurt his right hind leg. I think you know about it. It healed fine, and he is as good a racer as you may find in the whole of Ireland. But those people at the racing ring, what do you think they are saying! Horses without the least wee bit of a blemish on a leg they want, and they wouldn't allow my Charlie to be racing again. Annoying it is, I do say."

He really looks bothered now, Willy Cavanagh.

"As a working horse I am using Charlie now, together with my white Dolly."

"Och, and a great pity it is," Bridie says.

18

And then we all go home.

Mother sits in her favorite stone seat in the corner by the fire. She is watching the potatoes so they won't boil over. In another pot the bread is baking.

Little Carmel and Gerald are squeezed on the second seat, and cracking fresh hazelnuts from our bushes.

Through the kitchen window I see the postman riding up on his bicycle, and I give the sign: "POSTMAN!" I shout, so everybody around can hear, even in the back yard, and I run out. Whoever sees the postman first, gives the sign and we all run out then. He knows all the news, and nobody else passes our house all day long except the neighbors.

Dermot cycles around the villages all morning, from cottage to cottage, and then again in the afternoon. We do not have a post office in our village, so Dermot brings the mail from Kinvara village. If we want to send a letter, we just give it to him.

Mammy calls us into the kitchen for dinner. It is cabbage we are having, cooked together with bacon.

We say grace and sit down for the meal.

The turf fire from the hearth smells good. A pot of big potatoes hangs over the fire on long iron bars. The bars can be lowered or raised. If Mammy wants to cook something slowly, she raises the bar to a higher peg, and then the pot is farther away from the heat. But for quick cooking, she lowers the bar almost down to the burning turf, and then the flames lick up all around the pot and heat it very fast.

The water in the teakettle has been boiling, so now it hangs a bit higher. The bread in the pot is ready. Mammy makes two loaves of brown bread from whole wheat and from oatmeal every day, one in the morning, and one after dinner. When the dough is ready, Mammy cuts a cross into it. She says her grandmother always did it and it is to keep the hunger away from our door. Then she puts the dough

into the pot. She puts the pot on the fire, takes some of the glowing red-hot turf from the hearth, and puts it on top of the lid. The heat then comes from below and from above, and makes our bread crisp all over.

Bridie has just taken the lid and the hot ashes on top of it away from the pot, because the brown bread is ready. She takes it out of the pot and puts it on an iron grill.

"Can I take the bread to the yard for cooling?" asks Tom.

"I want to take it out!" says Johnny.

"I was first," says Tommy.

"I am taking it out anyway," answers Johnny. "You just scratch your nose when you put the bread on the wall," and he runs up to the bread.

"Easy, lads, don't be bold!" says Mammy now. "Tommy said it first, and Tommy it is. But don't you burn your fingers. There is time enough, we only need it in the evening."

Tommy takes the bread from the grill. He carries it out and puts it on the wall for cooling off. Yesterday he really scratched the tip of his nose on the stone wall when he put the bread up.

"The wall hit my nose," he complained.

Periwinkles for pocket money

"Bridie and Michael and Paddy, go and be fetching me some carrageen moss," Mammy says. "I will be cooking some pudding from it. And Michael, don't forget to roll up your pants in the water, and be taking your shoes off. Last time you were spoiling them almost, coming home all wet you were!"

We walk down to the shore. I like the smell of the seaweed, and when I lick my lips, they taste salty from the ocean air.

We step into the water, and walk over to the banks. The tide is out, and the banks are now above water. The red carrageen moss has been drifting in from the ocean, and we pick it out of the water. Mammy washes it, and then she cooks it with milk, and out comes a sweet jelly pudding. I like it very much. But when I have an upset stomach, Mammy cooks the carrageen moss for me with just plain water, and it sets my stomach right again. But then it does not taste so good, and I do not like it very much.

The water is still shallow, but soon the tide will be coming back, and so we don't go far out into the water. The banks are only a hundred yards from the shore.

"Michael," says Bridie, "where are your shoes?"

"On my feet, silly!" says Michael. But then he remembers:

"Och, bother!" he cries, "I surely forgot again to take them off!"

"You did. And your pants are *not* rolled up, either."

Michael winces.

"Isn't it disgusting," he says. But he goes on collecting carrageen moss with his pants not rolled up, and with his shoes on his feet.

"It's too late now anyway," he says.

The bank is covered with seaweed. We often collect it and put it on the fields. There are many chemicals in it that make the earth give better crops, only we don't have to buy it, we collect it from the sea. But today it is only carrageen moss we are after.

A small voice calls: "Bridie! Bridie!"

We look around, and there, over on the next bank, stands Gerald with his finger in his mouth, and smiling he is at us as if he had done something wonderful.

"Stay where you are, Gerald!" shouts Bridie. We drop our sack and the buckets and jump over the slippery rocks and through puddles until we reach Gerald.

Bridie is there first.

"Aren't you the boldest one!" she scolds Gerald, and takes him in her arms, and then she gives him a good slap.

"Always running after us, all the way from the cottage you were, you bold one, and with the tide coming in soon. What did you do out there!" "Bocky-money," he says, and smiles.

Gerald keeps his right fist closed. I open it, and not easy it is—
Gerald is a strong one. At last I force his hand open: a snail is in it.

Bridie carries Gerald back to the shore, and goes home with him.

"Fetch the carrageen moss!" she calls back to us.

Michael and I stay at the shore. We put all the carrageen moss into
the sack.

"We have much time," says Michael. "Let's collect periwinkles."
We look for them between the stones. They are small black snails,
and they feed on the seaweed that comes in with the tide.

When I pick a periwinkle from a stone, the snail draws back inside
the spiral shell. It can shut itself up quite tightly. Periwinkles can
live without water for hours.

We find many today, and we throw them into the pails. We sell
them to James Gaynor, over on the other side of the bay. And James
Gaynor sells them to the people in England and France. There they

really do eat snails! And they even like it! But we don't. We just collect them.

I am glad the people in England and in France like periwinkles and eat them, because Daddy allows us to keep the money we get for them from James Gaynor. It is our pocket money.

"Gerald must have overheard us talking about periwinkles and pocket money, Michael."

"Yes, and he thought he could get money for a single one. You know what, we'll bring him sweets, and tell him we got them for his periwinkle."

"Michael, do you think we could take the curragh boat ourselves today, for getting over the bay to James Gaynor? Then we needn't wait for Mick the Boat. He is after cuttin' the corn just now. I know, because he borrowed our horse after dinner. So he will not notice if we take the curragh."

"That is a great idea you are having, Paddy. And maybe we'll find a lobster for selling, too."

Lobsters are hard to find around our shore. We poke about underneath the big rocks where they like to be hiding. We try for a long time to stir one up—but we have no luck today.

We scoop up some salt water from the sea, and pour it over the periwinkles in our pails. It keeps them alive longer. Then we go back. Teresa and Johnny are hanging up the laundry on the stone fence when we come to our cottage. Michael whistles and gives them a sign to come over.

"We are going in the curragh to James Gaynor. Come along," we tell them.

We leave the sack with the carrageen moss in the kitchen for Mammy to find when she comes in. We go around our sugar beet field to Mick the Boat's cottage, and down to his shore.

There are the boats! The curragh lies upside down in the sand, looking like a small whale.

We are not allowed to go alone in the curragh really. It is dangerous, because it tips over easily.

"I know how to steer it," says Teresa. And Michael says he knows too. They have been with Mick the Boat in the curragh before. I say:

"We'd better get away before anybody sees us." We turn the curragh over. It is a very light boat indeed, just a wooden frame covered with tarred canvas. We pull it down into the water. Johnny and I step in first. Michael and Teresa hold the curragh. Then Teresa gets in. Michael gives it a push and swings himself into the boat. Teresa and I take the oars, Michael directs us, and we row away from the shore.

The curragh rocks pretty much. It jumps up and down because it is so light.

"There comes old Mrs. Curtin running," says Johnny all of a sudden.

She waves to us from far up the shore, and calls to us. We do not hear what she says, but we know for sure what she *means*.

Now she comes down to the shore, and we can hear her:

"Come back, children!" she calls. "You do be lost! Come back! Turn back! Turn!"

"She is always afraid for everybody, that Mrs. Curtin," says Michael. But I feel a little scared myself now—she might tell her son, and Mick the Boat will tell Daddy, he being his cousin. And the oars do not work as I am used to, they have very narrow blades and do not follow my strokes, and there is a current.

27

"We are drifting out to sea," says Johnny, and he looks afraid.

"No, we are not!" says Teresa angrily. "Why, you should have stayed home, if you have fear!"

"Och, don't act like Grace O'Malley," answers Johnny, "I wasn't even saying I am scared!"

"But you are, you are!" calls Teresa.

But Michael says: "Old Mrs. Curtin is still calling. Turning back we are." And Michael being the oldest, we turn back, and I am really glad we do. The current is very strong now, and we *are* drifting toward the sea.

Michael and Teresa take the oars. The way back to the shore is much harder than coming out. The wind has become stronger, too. The waves carry the curragh and throw it about a bit, it is very bumpy. Johnny and I hold on tight to the canvas sides. And it starts raining a bit. Michael and Teresa are rowing hard, they are sweating all over their faces. We do not talk any more at all. I just sit and hope we get back safely, and I smile at Johnny, so he won't get too scared, but I am scared myself.

Michael speaks up: "Look round, we are almost there. Nothing to worry about." And really, the shore is very near, and the curragh hits the sand, and out we jump and pull the boat after us, and are we happy!

We landed much too far down the bay, the current made the boat drift so much. Now we have to carry it back on our shoulders. We turn it upside down, and creep under it, and prop ourselves against it. "One, two, three, up," commands Michael. The curragh is very light. That's why only grown men are allowed to go out in it.

We walk back along the shore, with the curragh over our heads like a strange umbrella for four. Well, at least we won't get wet this way.

Finally we are back at Mick the Boat's shore. Teresa and I make the curragh fast, but Michael walks over to old Mrs. Curtin's cottage to tell her that we heard her warning and have turned around. And that we are sorry we took the curragh. And he leaves our periwinkles with her for her son to take over the bay to James Gaynor tomorrow.

We go home again. Hundreds of sea gulls fly over our heads. They are coming in from the sea, and they circle around, and then they settle down on the fields.

Tommy is driving the geese home. He waves and shouts: "Cead mile failté!" Tommy doesn't know much Irish yet, but he likes to say "Cead mile failté," because it means "A hundred thousand welcomes," and it is an old Irish greeting, and he thinks it is wonderful to greet someone one hundred thousand times.

Teresa is still annoyed because we turned back in the curragh, and because Johnny teased her about Grace O'Malley.

Grace O'Malley was a pirate queen in the Irish islands, almost four hundred years ago. She owned all the islands off our coast, and her castle still stands on one of them, on Inishmore.

Grace O'Malley, she had great courage, and was a great sea captain, and even when everybody else was afraid, she never was. Even in the worst storm she loved sailing around and brought her ship home safely.

Grace O'Malley attacked the Spanish ships and the English ships that came up the west coast of Ireland with cargoes for the port of Galway. The government of England declared her an outlaw and a pirate, and put a big price on her head. But they never captured her.

When Queen Elizabeth in London heard of the courageous pirate queen, and of the tricks she played on her captains and merchants, she laughed and sent her a letter, and invited her to England to the palace, and she promised her safe conduct. Grace O'Malley came, and they had a good time together. Queen Elizabeth asked her to stay in England, and said she would make her a countess. But Grace O'Malley said: "What would I want to be an English countess for, when I am Grace O'Malley and a queen on an Irish island?" And they parted on very friendly terms, and Grace O'Malley went back to her castle on the island of Inishmore.

It is a true story, but Teresa doesn't want to be teased with the name of Grace O'Malley. She talks about her often, and she loves her.

She has a story about Grace O'Malley in a book and she reads it over and over again.

When we come home, Mammy says: "Where have you been so long? You are late for tea." But of course she gives us our tea, and brown bread and butter and jam and a plateful of oatmeal porridge.

After tea, we kneel down and say our rosary. Mammy says the words first, and we repeat them after her.

And then we are sent off to bed.

We go to market to buy sheep

"It is half five, Paddy, time to go to the market. Wake up!" It is Daddy shaking me awake.

I put on my corduroy suit and my sandals. Everybody else is still asleep. Shall I tickle Michael's feet? He would know I did it this time. I'd better not tickle him.

Daddy is raking the ashes from the hearth. There are still glowing embers left from yesterday night. I run into the yard for more turf. It is very cold. The moon is still in the sky behind the clouds.

Daddy puts two new chunks of turf on the embers, and we two blow carefully from one side into them until the flame bursts out. Now the fire is in the hearth again for the day. I hang the kettle up, and the water is soon boiling. We have our tea and brown bread with butter and pumpkin jam on it.

Pete the Lorry comes with his truck.

Daddy fetches two turkeys and brings them out to Pete.

"It is a cold morning, all right," Pete the Lorry greets Daddy. Pete got his nickname "the Lorry" because he owns one, and works with it for other people. He already has four cattle and seven sheep in the back of his lorry, and now he puts our two turkeys in. "They are fine twelve-pounders," says Daddy, "I want to swap them for pullets at the market. I will meet you at the tea canteen."

Pete the Lorry puts his foot down on the gas pedal, and drives off to other cottages, collecting more sheep and cattle for the market.

Daddy and I take the bicycles from the shed. We have one man's bike, for Daddy, and two girls' bikes, for me and my brothers and sisters.

We mount and start on our way. First it is quite flat. But then we make a sharp turn at the crossroads, and now it goes uphill for a long time. We pass St. Patrick's well and I have to pedal hard to keep up with Daddy. But he notices it and stops, and we push our bicycles for a while.

The sun is coming up. From the road I can see our village, and behind the village, the bay where we tried to cross over to James

Gaynor yesterday. Mick the Boat will take our periwinkles along today. He can ride the highest waves in his curragh, he knows how to handle it. Mick has even been in curragh races.

Way out from the village, to the left, I see the steeple of our church in the trees.

A lane to the left goes even higher up the hill. There is a signpost, and it says: "Knockawuddy," the Hill of the Clown. Long ago, a very jolly man had his cottage up there. He loved clowning and making fun with the people, he was known for it all over the county. So the place was called after him, and it still has the same name. But we do not go up the clown's hill. We have arrived at the highest point of the road, and now we dash along downhill. I have to use my brakes and it is a pleasure, going so fast without pedaling.

Some trucks pass us now, and we meet other people on bicycles. Cattle and sheep are on the road, and all are going to market.

Soon we come to the market town. Another bend in the road, and we are there. It starts drizzling a bit. We dismount, and lean our bikes against a fence.

"Come with me, Paddy," says Daddy. We go to a blackthorn bush on the roadside, and Daddy cuts a nice long stick from it. "Here,

33

lad," he says to me, "it is your first day to the market, you want a stick to make the animals mind."

Then we walk to the market square. Trucks and donkey carts and automobiles and cattle and sheep are standing around. We find Pete the Lorry at the tea canteen. We all drink our mug of tea, and eat buns. Then Daddy takes his two turkeys, and he tells me to walk around for a while on my own, and to take a good look at the sheep.

I go to the sheep pens and watch the farmers and how they buy and sell. First they look at the teeth of the sheep to see if they are healthy.

Daddy is back very soon. "I sold the turkeys, but there are no pullets today," he tells me. "Mammy won't be happy about it."

We walk together along the sheep pens.

"It's a wet day we are having," Daddy says to a farmer who stands with his sheep.

"Wet it is," answers the farmer. And then they talk for a long time about the weather and about the harvest, and I don't really know whether Daddy wants to have a nice talk or whether he wants to buy sheep here or not.

"Do you sell already?" Daddy asks, and now I prick up my ears.

"Sure I do!"

Daddy looks at the teeth of a sheep and touches the wool.

"It's eight pounds of fine wool you'll be getting out of that sheep!"

"Maybe," answers Daddy, and walks on with me. "That wool

wasn't good enough, Paddy. Now when I look at the next sheep, you feel the wool too."

"Come here!" calls a man to us. "Buy, Mr. Curtin, you name the price!"

It is Joe Healy, I know him, he has many sheep. Daddy looks carefully at the sheep's teeth.

"Och, they are not the best sheep in the market today," he says.

"Don't say that," answers Joe Healy. "They are all purebred Galway sheep. I never had better ones in all my life. Look at this one, never had a lamb yet, good stock, you name the price. Pay me seven pounds!"

"It's too high," Daddy says, and walks on. I touch the wool, and it feels strong and fine at the same time. Joe Healy comes after Daddy, and holds out his hand:

"Six pounds and fifteen shillings," he says. "You'll get plenty of good wool out of these sheep, Mr. Curtin, and you know it yourself. Call it a bargain!" And he tries to clasp Daddy's hand, but Daddy holds it high up.

"Six pounds and five shillings it is," he says, "and not a shilling more, and I'll take four of them." It's Daddy now who holds out his hand. Joe Healy has his hands down now. But then he grasps Daddy's hand quickly. "It's a bargain!" he calls, and they clasp hands on it, and the sheep are ours.

"Paddy, drive the sheep over to our bicycles and watch them till Pete the Lorry comes for them. Use your blackthorn stick, keep them together, lad."

Keep them together, Daddy says. That's not so easy. They run in all directions, and I have a hard time of it, driving them to the bicycles. When I have two together, the other two are sure to hobble away. And all sheep look alike anyway.

Father stands back with his friends and watches me, because he wants me to learn helping him on market days. I am glad we didn't buy more sheep, four of them are just about enough for me to handle.

Daddy comes over. "You are doing pretty well for a first time, Paddy," he says. "I think keeping an eye on sheep on market day is harder than running the hundred-yard dash."

"It is," I answer.

Pete the Lorry's truck is pulling up. Pete opens a side door, and together we push our four sheep in. Pete writes down the markings our sheep have, so he doesn't mix them up with other sheep he is transporting today.

"Daddy, could I go to see my friend Thomas? Do you allow me to go now? I will be back in time for tea, surely."

"I don't see why you should not. If you go fast, it will not be more than one hour on the bike. Do not pedal up the corkscrew road, though. It's too steep, and you will do better going through Gort city. God be with you."

"God be with you," I say, and dash off.

Thomas is cutting the turf in the bog

I like to be on the road, alone on my bicycle. All I meet are three goats lying on the ground, and I have to go around the lazybones. Flocks of geese cackle at me from the roadside when I pass a cottage, and they run after me with loud gabbling.

A white horse looks over a stone fence at me, and I say: "Nice day, old Whitey," and give him a piece of sugar. I always carry some.

Soon I come to the town of Gort. It is still early, and I see very few people. I stop by a big shop window. Right in there stands the biggest tractor I have ever seen, a really gigantic one. It is painted in three different colors: orange, blue, and silver. Och, would that be a nice tractor to have! Willy Cavanagh owns a tractor together with his neighbor. But it is much, much smaller, and it is red only.

I have been in Gort before. Our whole class went to the song festival here in spring, and our school sang: "Nowhere greener pastures . . ." We sang it very well, and we each got a little flag with the green-white-orange colors of our country to wear on our jackets.

I go on, and after a while I come to the bog road, and it is very lonely. It looks so different from where we live. No grain fields, no potatoes, no sugar beets grow here, and I see no stone fences anywhere. I think it must be very poor land here, and I am not so sure I would like to stay here all my life.

Wherever I look, the bogland is covered with purple heather—it only grows on turf.

Right and left I see piles of brown turf cut out from the ground and left there for drying.

The bogland is soft and wet, and Daddy warned me not to step off the road, because I might sink into the ground up to my knees.

I learned about the turf in my reader. It says the bogland was all lakes and pools thousands of years ago. The water plants were rotting away and they sank down to the bottom and filled up the lakes until there was very little water left. The rotten plants were shut off from light and air, and so they got harder and turned slowly into a dark mass, and that is turf. It says in my book that up in County Donegal they found a little wooden house twenty-six feet down in the bog. About thirteen hundred years ago the inhabitants had left it when the turf grew up to the steps of the house. The turf grew

around and about it, two feet high every hundred years it grows. So in thirteen hundred years it grew twenty-six feet above the ancient dwelling.

A truck with turf passes me. I wave to the driver and he stops and I ask: "Do you know where the Scandlin family would be cutting the turf?"

"I do," he answers. "Just follow the road for a good three more miles. When you come to the first crossroads, you'll have to turn left. The Scandlin children are building up their turf pile by the road there for me to collect. You cannot miss them."

I go on for a long while, it seems to me. A few people are working in the bogland. Then I come to the crossroads and turn left, as the truck driver told me. Ahead of me, I see children working at a turf pile. They must be the Scandlins. I wave to them, and they shout to me: "Paddy, Paddy's coming! Paddy the Runner is here!"

"I made it," I say. "Isn't it the longest ride I ever had! Where is Thomas?"

"He is after cutting the turf right out there on the bog," says his sister Anne. "Paddy, I have been hearing you are the best runner in school. Surely it won't take long now, and you will be sent to the Olympic Games for running for Ireland."

"Och, that will be a long time yet, but I would like to try, honest to goodness I would." I lean my bike against the turf pile and go over the ditch to the bogland, but Anne starts talking again.

"Paddy, to the market you went today! Och, I wish I would be going there. I never went, it's always the men who are going. Tell me. . . ."

That is enough chatter for me, and I walk over to Thomas.

"Thomas!! Thomas!" I call out to my friend.

"Paddy!" he calls back and waves. I walk up, and we shake hands.

"How do you like it back here, cutting the turf?"

"I like it well. We are getting electricity in the cottages out here. They are putting the poles up now, and then we will have electric light, and father is buying a radio set, he is."

"You have been late in getting electricity. We're having it for years and years in our village!"

"You know, so many people around here didn't care for electricity, but now the majority want it, and so we get it."

Thomas takes his wooden cutting spade, and cuts deep into the wet ground. Where there was turf, there is now a pool of blackish water. Thomas throws the dripping chunks off to both sides of the little ditch he is making. When all the water has dripped off, his brothers and sisters take the pieces and pile them into little stacks of five each, for drying. There they stay until they are all dry, and then they are heaped on the roadside for taking away.

Thomas brings the turf for his own family home in their donkey cart. But most of the turf is sold to places where there is no bogland, and then it is carried away in trucks, like when Daddy buys some.

"I think it's a mug of tea we are wanting now," says my friend. "Got matches with you?" "No," I say. "Oh well," says Thomas, "I'll find some." And he puts his hand into the left pocket of his pants and reaches all the way down, almost to his boots.

"What kind of pockets do *you* have!" I ask.

"Och, that's the expanding kind of pocket. I was having big holes in my pockets, so my valuables always slid down my legs. Out they went and were lost. These leprechauns got mighty rich on me. But now I take a piece of string, and bind it tight around the ankle, and whatever slides down *now* stops right there."

Thomas really brings up a box of matches. He takes four turf pieces and lays them in a square. In the middle he piles little branches of dried heather and flaky turf. He has a teakettle of water with him, and from his shirt pocket he takes tea and sugar, and we blow the fire up and soon the water is boiling, and we drink from

Thomas' mug, and eat the fig biscuits which I bought at the market.

"Would you be coming to the hurling match tomorrow?" I ask Thomas. "You know, we are after beating our cousins, and you should be on our team again, and have dinner with us."

"Thank you, Paddy, for inviting me. But my uncle from America, he is mother's younger brother, he is visiting us, and tomorrow after Mass he is driving to Shannon Airport, for going back in an airplane to America. All the family is going along to the airport to bid him farewell. Have you ever been seeing those big planes on the ground in Shannon Airport, Paddy?"

"No, I haven't ever. But I see them flying out to sea often."

"My uncle will take us first to Kildare, so that he can look at the national horse studs, you know, Paddy, where all the famous race horses are bred. And perhaps we might even go over the Shannon River and visit the hydroelectric works down there. But next Sunday I surely can come, and with pleasure it will be, Paddy."

43

The haunted cottage

The tea is warming us up. We talk some more, and I am thinking of going home again. Thomas tells me how to go back.

"The short way is past the haunted cottage," he says.

"I didn't know there was a haunted cottage on the road."

"Oh yes, there is!" says Thomas, "it is the one with the broken chimney, right in front of the old oak trees. You will see old Jack Dougherty there, working on the road he is. I am sure he will be telling you scary stories. Never mind him. But when you come to the haunted cottage, just say your magic words."

"What magic words?" I ask.

"Och, you do not know the magic words? You better learn them, Paddy:

> "Rum fum boodle boo
> Ripple dipple nitty dob
> Dum doo doodle coo
> Raffle taffle chitty boo . . .

"Shall I say them again for you?"

"Oh blather!" I answer. "It is *you* be trying to scare me."

"Well, Paddy, you needn't believe me, but they say old Jack Dougherty has seen a fight between the greenjacket fairies and the redjacket ones with his own eyes, when he came home from the inn the other night. He says he saw it quite clearly, I was told, although it was a misty night and the moon was hiding behind the clouds. The greenjackets were winning and old Jack Dougherty gave a big shout to encourage them, and just then he was flung into a ditch and didn't see anything anymore. The redjackets were angry at him, he says, because he sided with the greenjackets, and that's why they flung him into the ditch."

I must be going now. We say goodbye, and we wave to each other, and I say goodbye to his sister and brothers, and then I am on my bicycle again.

44

The road goes downhill all the way here, and there are a few deserted cottages around already, many more than in my village. Ever since the Great Famine a hundred years ago, people go on leaving our island for England and America, and the cottages rot away, and they look sad, and the curse of the crow is on them: those black birds—once they settle on the roof of a deserted cottage, they eat away at the thatch and won't go away again from the ruin. Those old rotting houses, I don't like them.

Which one did Thomas say it was? With the broken chimney, and the old trees behind. . . . There are the old trees . . . and there is the cottage with the broken chimney in front of them. The haunted cottage it is.

"Dipple doodle dumdee dock. . ." Oh blather, I am not going to be scared, I am not! I put the brakes on, and I stop and jump from my bike. Shall I go over and peek in?

"Raffle tipple top!" I call out as loud as I can.

"Caw! Caw! Caw!

"Caw! Caw! Caw!"

I start back with a scare. Hundreds of crows suddenly fly off with awful cries. They fly over the cottage, back and forth, and "Caw! Caw! Caw!" they cry with their horrible voices.

I leap on my bicycle, and race off down the road. I turn my head to look back at the deserted cottage and the crows—and fly right over my bike into the ditch.

I sit up and rub my shin. It hurts, and my left wrist hurts, and my whole left side hurts. My bike is on the ground, I get up and look it over: the front wheel is all crooked.

How did *that* happen to me!

I didn't see the bend in the road when I was trying to look back at the haunted cottage, and then it must have been that I steered right into the ditch. Och, six eggs to Thomas an' half a dozen o' them rotten for telling me about the haunted cottage! And that old Jack Dougherty—and he wasn't even there!

A nice walk I will be having, wheeling my ruined bike to the blacksmith, and my wrist hurting, and all my pocket money will be going for the repair, and my half crown from Daddy too.

The bicycle wants to go to the left side all the time, where the ditch is, because of the crooked bend in the front wheel.

It starts drizzling. That's all I need now, rain! I am getting really tired, and glad I am when I come to Kinvara village, where the blacksmith lives.

Tim O'Glaidy is rolling out a cartwheel from the smithy.

"Paddy me lad," he calls, "what's ailing you, you walk crooked!"

"It's my bicycle walking crooked," I answer, "please, can you repair it?"

"I can," answers Tim O'Glaidy, "I'll fix it for you all right. Looks as if you went into a ditch."

"I did indeed," and that is all I say. It wouldn't do to be telling the smithy that it happened because I was looking back at a haunted cottage!

"Can I wait for it?" I ask.

"I am sorry, lad, but I'll not be fixing it today. Willy Cavanagh's tractor was breaking down today, and I am making a new piece for the axle."

The blacksmith is heating a piece of iron in his fireplace. He holds it on long prongs into the fire with his left hand. In his right hand he holds a chain, which is connected to a long wooden pole. When he pulls the chain, the horsehide bellows on the other side blow a lot of air into the fire. The flame shoots out, and the sparks fly right up to the ceiling. The fire gets very hot then, and makes the iron piece gleaming red and soft. The blacksmith takes it with his long tongs to the anvil and hammers the soft piece into any shape he wants.

Willy Cavanagh comes in, and Tim O'Glaidy tells him it will be another two hours before the new piece is ready. "I will have to work late after tea today on it, tomorrow is Sunday."

"I do appreciate it!" says Willy. I tell him about my misfortune, and he says: "I'll bring you on the bike to my house, from there you can walk home, it isn't far."

"Thank you, Willy Cavanagh," I say, and off we go, with me sitting on the frame in front of Willy.

Mr. Cavanagh is standing on the ladder. He is thatching the roof of his pigsty.

"Look who is coming," he says, "Paddy the Runner, and saving his legs he is for the big race!"

"Ah, teasing you are, Mr. Cavanagh," I say, and I tell him what happened, but not much about the haunted cottage. Mr. Cavanagh puts a new layer of straw on the roof. Then he bends a hazelnut stick double like a hairpin, and pushes the ends deep into the layer. That holds the thatch down, and even a strong wind can't blow it off the roof.

On top of the first layer comes a second one, and Mr. Cavanagh flattens and smooths the straw with a nailed brush. In the end he sprays blue-stone liquid over the thatch: it makes it waterproof and it is poisonous so the insects won't get into the thatch and eat it and make it rot.

48

"Very sunny it has become just now," Mr. Cavanagh says. "Just the right weather for thatching. But there are rainclouds coming up, you'd better be on your way, lad. And give my regards to the family."

"Thanks, I will," I say, "and thank you, Willy Cavanagh, for the ride."

I am hurrying now, because the rainclouds are coming near very fast. All of a sudden a shower comes down, a real one. It pours, and soaks me right through.

I meet the traveling shop, coming back from its rounds. Every Saturday afternoon it comes to us, and Mammy buys tea and sugar and salt and raisins, and loaves of white bread, so she doesn't have to go bicycling into Kinvara so often for things.

Right behind the traveling shop I see Captain running. He barks wildly at the truck, and races it. He does it every time. But now he sees me, and he stops and wags his tail, and comes up and jumps at me, and licks my cheeks. And I give him a hug.

Captain is a very good Shetland sheep dog. We don't really need him very much for the sheep, because they always graze in fenced-in fields, but he watches them and their little lambs when we drive them to other fields, and at night, when the foxes come out from their holes.

I love Captain's soft fur with the big frill around his neck.

The rainclouds have moved on, back to where I just came from. It must be raining now on Mr. Cavanagh's new thatch, and a bother it is. But where I am, the sun is breaking through. I turn round and see a beautiful rainbow in the sky against the dark clouds. It is the third one today. I see the beginning of the rainbow. I

think it comes from the lake behind our well, and it ends over on the west side right in the sea.

At last I come to our cottage. It is getting dark now, and I am really glad I am home again. Nobody is outside, only the turkeys making a fuss and hopping around on the stone wall.

Everybody is sitting around the fire and they are long after finishing tea. Mammy has saved me some bacon boiled with cabbage and potatoes from dinner, and she warms it up for me over the hearth. She knew I wouldn't have a warm meal all day long.

"Where is the bike?" Teresa wants to know, because she uses it most, and she has seen me coming back on foot. I say: "It's the leprechauns spoiled it for me." Teresa says: "What's *that* nonsense you are talking?" and Mammy says not to frighten little Carmel and Gerald, and to talk straight, and to tell what happened all day long.

Most of all I tell about the haunted cottage, and the magic words,

50

and how I was thrown into the ditch all of a sudden, and I wonder how it happened and who did it to me.

Michael says: "It surely wasn't the redjackets and it wasn't the greenjackets either. It was your stupidity, not looking where you were going, I am sure." But Tommy and Johnny say they want to learn the magic words, and I remember the first line and tell them: "Rum Fum Boodle Boo. . ."

Daddy says: "It is a pity you didn't peek into that cottage. You might have found a crock of gold there. You know the leprechauns went about the country at night and into people's houses. There they clipped little pieces of the gold and gold coins they found, and hid them away, and so they got rich. Well, anyway, it's too late *now*."

To church, and then we play hurling

"It's a lovely day," I hear Mammy say. "Get yourself ready for church."

I rack my hair, and put a tie on over my white shirt. We all put our Sunday suits on, and Mammy and Bridie have even more flowers on their dresses today than on weekdays.

Teresa stays home with little Carmel and Gerald. She is minding the children, and will be going to second Mass, after we come home.

"Have you all your pennies in your pockets?" Daddy is asking, and he makes sure we do not forget the money for church collection. Then we go up the road to St. Colman's church.

Some people come on bicycles, and some come by automobile, and the O'Shaugnessys, they ride in their jaunting car with the donkey pulling them. But the O'Malley family from the Meadow of the Wise Men, they come in a horse carriage, and pretty it is!

The church is hidden away behind the huge trees all around, only the steeple peeks out. The barley field behind the church belongs to Daddy. He was cutting the corn there yesterday, after he came back from the market.

In church we have a big statue of our patron saint Colman. Long, long ago, he lived in our county.

Canon Galway never waits a minute after half ten. He says Mass in three different churches in the neighborhood, so that everybody can come to one. He travels from church to church in his car. Master Moylan is here, too. He helps our Canon put on his vestments.

All the children sit in the front rows, but Bridie sits with Mammy, and Michael sits with Daddy.

The bells stop ringing, nobody whispers any longer, and Canon Galway comes in, and the altar boys are with him. They swing the censer with the incense, and Holy Mass begins.

After Mass, Daddy and Mammy stand around on the road and talk with their friends and with the neighbors about everything.

Bridie meets her girl friends. But we others go home, and I help little Carmel and Gerald climb the stone fence.

"Gerald," I say, "I sold your periwinkle, and look what I got for it!" and I give him a piece from the chocolate I bought at the market yesterday.

He smiles even more than usual, and grabs the chocolate and puts it in his mouth, with a piece of the paper still on it.

In the pasture I try to ride our donkey, and he throws me off again, as always. But Johnny he lets mount, and the two trot away.

Little Carmel and Tommy play with their pet lamb Bob. Bob's mother died when he was born. He was very lonely, and bleating day and night. So my parents decided that Tommy and little Carmel should be the stepparents of the lamb. They played all day long with him, and patted him, and gave him milk from a bottle. Bob is now quite big, but he still doesn't go with the other sheep. He is always kept home or in the field next to our house, and Tom and little Carmel take care of him. They even play tag with the lamb. Only when Gerald comes near him does the lamb run away. Gerald puts paper in the lamb's mouth. He thinks everybody should eat paper, because *he* likes it so much. But Bob does *not* like paper, why would he!

Mammy calls us in for dinner. We say grace and begin to eat. First we get barley broth. Then everybody gets a big chunk of boiled beef, with carrots, and onions, and chopped cabbage, and boiled potatoes.

When Mammy makes boiled beef, it tastes wonderful, it is *everybody's* favorite dish. Beets I do not care for much, but my beef I keep watching. I sit between little Carmel and Gerald, and Gerald, he is a grabber, and a big beef-eater he is. He gobbles his meat down and then he just grabs mine. He tries to, anyway. But he has no luck. I say:

"Want some of my beef, Gerald?" He stares at my plate and says: "I do. I do."

"Don't be bold, Gerald," says Mammy. "You had your own beef, eat the cabbage now." But cabbage he doesn't care for, and he still wants my beef. I hold out a piece in the palm of my hand. Just when he snaps at it, I push a piece of paper forward which I have hidden between my fingers. I push it right into Gerald's open mouth, and he spits it out and is very angry.

"Don't be bold now, both of you!" says Daddy, and now we behave.

Afterwards, it's carrageen pudding. And we drink big glasses of fresh water from the well with our meal.

"The laundry is dripping on my head!" Johnny complains.

"It is not!" says Bridie sharply. "You are making a fuss just to annoy us. It's only moist, and not wet, and you know it!"

After saying grace, Michael and I and Tommy and Johnny take our hurling sticks. We walk over to our cousins'. Linda stands at the stone fence. "Here come the Lowry Meaghers!" she greets us.

"Don't you make fun of us," says Michael. "Make fun of your brothers. Didn't *they* lose against us last Sunday?"

"They sure did, but they won't this time, not with Tony takin' part today."

Lowry Meagher was the greatest hurler of all time, and we are no Lowry Meaghers, but we are not bad players, not enough to make fun of.

All our cousins are home today. Tony is there, who is already eighteen and works on the road. And Noreen, and Mary, and Michael, and Patrick, and Joseph, and Bernadette, and Jerry, and Rita, and Dermot, who is only six months old. They are eleven brothers and sisters, we are only nine.

In the field just behind the cottage, we take our jackets off and start. We are three on each side, and the two goalkeepers. Michael and I and Johnny and Tommy are our team. Joseph and Jerry and

Patrick and Tony play against us. In regular games there are of course fifteen players on each side.

My Uncle Peter Curtin is the umpire. "Pity it is you are not more today," he says.

"When we fall over each other, six is enough for me," says Jerry.

"Well," says Uncle Curtin, "in olden times two hundred men played on each side, and true it is."

"And a fine mix-up it must have been, when four hundred players fell over each other, Uncle," I say.

I am good at speed, and I get to the ball quickly and I can tap it along fast. And Michael plays even better. But it's not much good it does us today, with big Tony playing on the other side, and hitting the ball into our goal so often. And Tommy is not much good as a goalkeeper, he doesn't even see them coming sometimes. So it is soon three to one for the Peter Curtins, and after thirty-five minutes the game is over, and it is eight for them and three for us.

Last week *we* won, and so it is a tie. But next Sunday my friend Thomas will play with us, I am sure we will win again then.

The Road of the Flying Dishes

"What do we do now?" It's Johnny asking.

Michael has an idea. "Let's go to Dun Guaire!" It is a long way off to the castle, but we decide to go there anyway. Only Tony and the girls stay behind.

We take all the short cuts, and we jump over stone fences and ditches, and run a lot, and in half an hour we arrive in the field behind Canon Galway's big house in Kinvara village. We walk quietly along the big wall around the house, and then we run along the quay. The tailor has his workshop here, he made Daddy's good suit. Over on the other side of the quay on a little hill above the bay stands the fortress of King Guaire.

He was the great king of all the western provinces of Ireland in olden times. The castle was often destroyed and rebuilt, and now it is almost a ruin, but one can still go up to the tower and look out into the land.

We call the castle by its Irish name, Dun Guaire, that means Fortress Guaire. It has a very thick and high stone wall, and Caretaker Tom has the key to the gate. He lives nearby and he sees to it that the castle is always in good repair.

Tom is not around today. We call his name, but there is no reply. We climb over the low stone fence at the bottom of the hill, and run up to the gate. I hear a muffled noise, as if some animal were inside. I press my face against the iron bars and peek.

"Look!" I call to the others, "a black-and-white calf is grazing in the castle court."

"Whose is it?" Johnny wants to know.

"King Guaire's it might be," Michael teases.

"It might and it mightn't!" It is old Tom, who says it. He comes up to the gate from inside the wall, and we greet him.

58

"Sunny day it is, boys, and mighty nice of you to come and visit me." Old Tom is talking to us through the bars of the iron gate. He opens it and lets us into the court, where his calf grazes.

"Want to go up to the watchtower?" he asks us. "You should see far today, with those clear-weather clouds up in the sky."

Of course we want to; we go up the winding staircase to the big banquet hall of King Guaire, where he always invited so many guests to the great feasts he gave. Of course, only the walls are there now, that's all that is left. The windows are very small because there was no glass in those days, and it was safer, too, when enemies attacked.

We climb up to the guard's walk around the top of the tower. Through the narrow fire slits we look out over the land. We see our whole parish all along the coast, and I can see far out into the ocean. Even the three Aran Islands we see today! The left one is Inisheer, then comes Inishmaan, and the big one to the right is Inishmore Island, where the pirate queen once had her castle.

"Look down there!" calls Michael from the other side. I come over to him, and he points to the southwest. The Round Tower of Kilmacduagh can be seen today!

We look around for some time, and then we go down again. Tom the caretaker is sitting on a stone bench, and smoking a pipe.

"I have seen the Round Tower," says Johnny.

"You have, have you," answers Tom. "Has any one of you boys been to Kilmacduagh?" Nobody has.

"And do you know about the Road of the Dishes leading from this castle down to Kilmacduagh?"

Nobody knows.

"Sit down here on the grass," says old Tom, and he tells us the story:

"You know who King Guaire was, the first master of this castle. He lived in the seventh century, more than thirteen hundred years ago, I should say. A fine and a generous king he was. They say his right arm was longer than his left, from giving away so many things to needy people.

"Now this castle was King Guaire's summer residence, here he came to spend the summer days by the sea.

"One day the king and his guests were sitting down to a great meal, up there in the banquet hall you have just been seeing. The king said grace, and he ended up with these words: 'And Lord, if there be anyone in my kingdom more worthy of such a meal than we, it is my earnest wish that he receive it instead of we!'

"Well, what do you think? The minute he spoke the last word, it happened! The dishes were whisked off the table by an unseen force. They just flew away: plates and bowls and cups and saucers and knives, and of course all the wonderful food, too: soup, and the roast geese, the lobsters and the vegetables and the many desserts, and all the wine.

"Even the tablecloth flew through the air before their very eyes, and all went in the same direction, to the southwest.

"The guests and the king were stunned, but Guaire recovered quickly from his shock and commanded: 'The horses, bring the horses, quick!'

60

"The king and his friends raced off after the dishes, down the road to the southwest.

"Now there lived at that time a very holy man in our County Clare. He was just about to build his hermitage with a young monk. The name of the holy man was Colman. . . ."

"Isn't that Saint Colman, our patron saint?" Johnny asks.

"Don't ask questions now," Cousin Joseph says. "We want to hear the story!"

And Tom continues: "Now Colman and his friend had just said Mass on that day, and were about to sit down to their meal. A poor meal it was indeed. A piece of bread and an egg and a mug of water. The young monk said:

" 'We work so hard in the service of God Almighty, and look how little we have to eat, and the same it is every day for months and months, and not always an egg either!'

"Colman answered him: 'Do not grumble, friend. God provides us with a meal worthy of our holiness.'

"Suddenly, dishes and dishes full of good things came flying through the air and on to their table, why, even a fine tablecloth came sailing along! Colman and the young monk were surprised indeed; they said grace again and sat down, and started eating heartily. And they did not waste many words or any time either.

"Well, they hadn't finished with the first course, when they heard horses approaching. The young monk was afraid, but Colman said: 'Sure, no harm will come to us!' That very moment the hoofs of all the horses stuck to the road, and they couldn't move a bit, until Colman and his friend had eaten.

"King Guaire dismounted and came up to Colman. From what had happened, he understood that this must be a mighty holy man. He embraced him, and they had a long talk, and the king asked Colman to become bishop of the whole province. And Colman built a beautiful cathedral around the place where they had eaten that miraculous meal, and he called it Kilmacduagh.

"And you know, a road down there is still called Boher na Maes, and what would that be in English?"

"The Road of the Dishes," I say. I do know that much Irish.

"That's right. Now, Johnny, what you were asking before, you are right too. This Colman became our patron saint, and it's him you have a statue of in your church."

Michael whispers in my ear: "Dishes don't fly, and horses' hoofs don't get stuck to the road. A fairy tale it is, and all blarney."

I ask Tom: "Is it a true story?"

"It might be, and again it mightn't," he answers. "But one thing is sure and true history: this castle here *did* belong to King Guaire once in the seventh century.

"Well, it is time for me to be going home, and you have a very long way to your home! Come back at any time, and visit me again."

"Thank you, Tom," we say, "thanks very much!"

When we come back to Kinvara village, I remember that Mammy has asked me to bring a box of matches, and that I want to go to the smithy and take my bicycle home. Johnny comes with me and we go to the store.

We have never been in this store before, because the girls always do the shopping. But I say to the owner of the store: "Please, can I have a big packet of matches?"

62

"Sure, my lad." And then she says: "Now who would you be, I have never seen you here."

"I am Johnny," my brother says. And I say, "I am Paddy, Patrick Curtin's boys we are."

"I am surely glad to meet two Curtin boys, my lads. And what else will it be for you, then?"

"A chocolate bar, please," says Johnny. And I want a chocolate bar too.

Johnny holds out his pennies.

But she says: "You may keep your pocket money this time, my lads. It's for coming to my store for the first time. I hope I will be seeing you often now."

"How much are the matches?" I ask.

"You don't pay me at all, Paddy Curtin. You see this book here? That's where I write down what your family is buying. And then your father or your mother comes by and pays for the lot once every few weeks. And the trustiest people they are, your parents. You just grow up to be like them, and you'll be all right the rest of your life."

"She is a nice lady, she is," says Johnny, after we leave the store.

"Yes, she is," I say, and we eat our chocolate bars and go over to the smithy. My bike is ready and it costs me two shillings for the repair. I take Johnny on the handlebars in front of me, and we ride home.

When we get there nobody is home. I cut a big slice of brown bread and put a thick load of jam on it. Johnny wants one too, we are really hungry.

"I think they are all out cuttin' the corn in the third field," I say to Johnny. "Let's go to the shore and hit pebbles with our hurling sticks."

Teresa and Tommy are there: "We are just getting some carrageen moss for the calves' fodder," says Teresa. "You can help us."

I don't like the idea of working again today, and Tommy runs away with us, over to the pebble shore.

We jump over big rocks, and wade through puddles, and the rocks are slippery, and I slip and fall. I sit up on the rock and rub my knee. Tommy suddenly gives a shout: "Lobster! Lobster!"

I am up and over to him, and he points under a rock and says: "There, it just crept in there!"

I don't believe it, but with my hurling stick I poke around under the rock . . . and there it comes creeping out, a mighty big lobster indeed, and then it runs away. But I am quicker. I catch it with my hands, just the right way like Joe of the Pond has taught me, so it cannot hurt me with its big shears, they are dangerous ones. In the middle of the shell and behind the head I grip it tightly and hold it up in the air for Johnny and Tommy to look at.

I carry my lobster to Teresa, and she gives me a bucket to throw it in. It cannot climb up the smooth walls of the bucket.

"Let me carry the lobster home," says Teresa. "Let's hurry now, the tide will be coming in soon."

Big black clouds are blowing in from the sea. We climb up the old stone wall on the shore. A storm is coming up from the ocean. Far out we see the lightning in the dark sky. It's time to go home. "One! Two! Three!" I count out, "Jump!" and we jump down the wall and run up the lane and back to our cottage.

We are going to the tower of Kilmacduagh

Mammy wakes us at seven o'clock, because vacation is over and
school starts again.

Before going off to school we must get the day's water. So, after
breakfast, I bridle our donkey Jacko and harness him to the cart.
Michael and Teresa put the big water barrel on it.

It is one mile to our well, and we go there every day for fresh
water. The well is surrounded on three sides by a stone wall, and
four steps lead up to the platform. Michael pumps, and Teresa pours
the buckets of water into the barrel. After a while it is my turn to
pump.

When the barrel is full, Michael throws a heavy sackcloth over it,
so the water won't splash out too much. But then he races Jacko on
the way back, and the water does splash a lot, and we get wet.

"Rack your hair and off to school, it is getting late!" Mammy calls.
Teresa and Johnny and Tommy and I start off together. We have it
near to school, only thirty minutes. But from other villages and
cottages my friends have to walk an hour and more.

Our schoolhouse is very new. It was built by the government. We all sit together in the same classroom, except, of course, for the little ones. We are seated according to our ages, so every group can work on the same book.

"Dia's Muire dhib a phaisti," says Master Moylan, our teacher. It means in English, "God and Mary be with you, children." And we answer: "Dia's Muire duit is Padraig, a Mhaighstir,"—"God and Mary and Patrick be with you, Master."

Master Moylan goes on talking to us in Irish. Every day we read and write half an hour in Irish and half an hour in English. Geography and arithmetic we have in Irish and English. And when we start school, we get our Irish names.

Master Moylan unfolds a map of Ireland in many colors. It looks as if it had been made by hand.

"Master Moylan, who did this map, please?" I ask.

"I did it during vacation, Padraic, and great fun it was, too."

Master Moylan does many things. First, he is our schoolmaster. He has his own fields to work, and he helps his wife and his mother-in-law with their big grocery store and their hotel in Kinvara village. And then he vests the Canon in church. And when the government in our capital, Dublin, sends someone down to our village, he shows him around in his car.

Master Moylan points to the map with his ruler and explains: "We live in County Clare, right on the border of County Galway. Now Fergus, how many counties does Ireland have?"

"Thirty-two," says Fergus, "but six counties in the north are still governed by England, sort of, they haven't given them up yet."

"Why is that, Mary Malone?"

"Because England believes the six counties in the north belong to her, but we believe they belong to Ireland. Master Moylan, why do the English believe that the six counties in Northern Ireland should not belong to our Republic?"

"That is a good question, Mary. Well, you know, we are an island and England is an island, just across the waters to the east of our country. Now the English conquered Ireland a long, long time ago, and we Irish people had very bad times because of that, and we had no rights at all in our own country. Of course we didn't like it, having foreigners treat us so badly in our own land. And so, all through the centuries, we made rebellions and fought for our freedom. The English said they had conquered us, that's why they wanted to stay. But we say that every people in the world has the right to be free, and that's why we didn't give up in our fight for freedom. Now, when did we have the last of those great rebellions?"

I know it, of course. Today Master Moylan asks only very easy questions, it seems.

"In 1915!" I answer.

"1916!!" shouts the class. "Well, 1916, then," I say. "There were many battles in Dublin city and all over the country. The rebellion failed, and many leaders were shot by the English. But from then on, Ireland got more and more of her rights back. And in 1949 we became completely independent and our name is the Republic of Ireland, Poblacht Na H'eireann."

"Padraic, you have given us a whole history, that was fine! And now one last question: Who was the famous leader in the rebellion of 1916 who became our first Prime Minister?"

"Eamon de Valera!" we all shout. Why does Master Moylan put such easy questions today, I am wondering. Perhaps he hasn't prepared for a real day of learning for us?

"It seems we are having a little more time in school than I thought," says Master Moylan, "so let's sing. What would be a fine song about our Irish Republic? Sean, you tell me."

" 'Nowhere greener pastures,' please," says Sean.

" 'Nowhere greener pastures' it be," answers Master Moylan, and he conducts while we stand up and sing:

Nowhere greener pastures, This is holy Ireland
Nowhere browner hills, Where your fathers trod;
Nowhere bluer rivers This the land where Patrick
Fed by sparkling rills. Told them first of God.

 Love her, do not leave her
 O'er the world to roam.
 Ireland needs her children
 Work for her at home.

Táinig Naoṁ Pádraig go h-Éirinn sa ḃliaṅ 432
St. Patrick came to Ireland in the year 432

I hear a truck stopping outside. I stretch my neck and see it is Pete the Lorry. He honks his horn three times. Now what would Pete the Lorry be collecting at the school?

"Miceal, Sean, Cieram, Fergus, Dermot, Padraic, help me bring some benches from the other rooms to the truck for you to sit on. This is a surprise for all of you! We won't have regular school today, we are going to Kilmacduagh for seeing the Round Tower!"

"Hurray! Hurray!" we shout. So that's why we had no proper school today. We climb into the truck and sit on the benches, and Pete drives us. We pass our cottage. Mammy and little Carmel and Gerald are with the pet lamb out in the field.

"Kilmacduagh! Kilmacduagh!" we call to them. Farther on, Daddy and Michael are working in the sugar-beet field: "Kilmacduagh! Kilmacduagh!" we shout again together. Daddy laughs and waves his cap. And whenever we see people we shout, "Kilmacduagh! Kilmacduagh!"

In Kinvara, the truck stops at the convent school.

"Padraic and Sean, go in and tell Sister Carmel we are here, and are they ready." We knock at the door of Sister Carmel's classroom.

70

"Master Moylan sends his compliments," I say, "and would you be ready with your class?"

"Thank you, Padraic Curtin," says Sister Carmel. "Sit down, both of you. We will be ready in a few minutes. We were just talking about another Padraic. Well then, when Patrick came to Ireland, he was a missionary, and that means he wanted to make all the people in Ireland Christians. They were pagans before.

"Now Patrick was a clever man, he first went to the kings and chiefs. Once he had converted *them*, the people soon followed.

"Patrick had a favorite little plant, a three-leaf clover which re-sembled a cross. As you all know, this is the shamrock. It grows only in Ireland. And when St. Patrick became the patron saint of Ireland, the shamrock of course became our national emblem.

"And now let's hurry, we are all going to the abbey and the Round Tower of Kilmacduagh!"

"Hurray!" answers everybody in class. They go in a second truck, and off we are again on the road to Kilmacduagh.

We pass the castle Dun Guaire, and then we travel along a lane to the southwest. Master Moylan says: "This lane would be. . . ."

"The Road of the Flying Dishes!" calls Johnny.

"And what would you be knowing about it, Johnny?"

Johnny tells the whole story which Tom the caretaker had told us yesterday.

"I wish they would be flying after us now," says Teresa.

"You would have to be as holy as St. Colman!" says Roisin Moylan.

Bernadette wants to sing. "Let's sing 'The Pillar Towers,' " she sug-gests, and we sing the song:

> The pillar towers of Ireland—
> How wondrously they stand
> By the lakes and rushing rivers
> Through the valleys of our land . . .

We come to Kilmacduagh, and the trucks stop at the stone wall around the ruined abbey and the cemetery with all the old crosses. There is a narrow opening in the wall, and we step through it, one after the other.

71

The tower is really all round, and on top are six windows, but I cannot see any door for going inside.

Master Moylan explains that the tower is very high, one hundred and twelve feet. "It doesn't stand quite straight," he says. "Look carefully and you will see. It leans two feet to the left side. Now look at that big window, the one nearest to the ground. It isn't a window at all, it is the entrance to the tower."

"Entrance! It looks so small. How can anybody squeeze in through there?" Fergus is asking.

"Well, Fergus, this entrance is over six feet high. It looks so small because it is high up, and we are far away."

"How did people climb up when they wanted to go into the tower?" Maureen is the next one to ask, but we all have questions. It is all so strange.

"Now let me tell you from the beginning," says Master Moylan. "This Round Tower is very old, almost a thousand years old. You remember about St. Colman—he built the abbey over there, and his little hermitage, and later the church and cathedral. All the ruins are still here, you can all go exploring afterwards. Colman called the place Kilmacduagh. Now the name of Colman's father was Duagh, and 'Kil,' what does 'Kil' mean?"

" 'Kil' means church," says Mary Malone.

"And 'Mac' . . . Tommy, would you know?"

"Son," says Tommy. He never speaks long sentences.

"Well, and now for Kilmacduagh, Johnny?"

"I don't know," he answers.

"Come on," says Mary Malone, "it's easy: 'Church of the Son of Duagh' it is."

"Yes indeed," says Master Moylan. "He called the church after himself and after his father, for he was proud to be the son of Duagh.

"A few hundred years after Saint Colman, the Danish raiders came to Ireland in their long boats from over the sea, all the way from Scandinavia. They landed on our coast. That was in the ninth century. They attacked the churches and houses, where they were after precious things.

72

"Now the monks had a good idea. They built tall round watchtowers so they could see the Danes approaching long before they attacked. Inside the tower here there are five floors, with trap doors between each floor. On every floor they made just one window, each one facing in a different direction. But the top floor has six windows, so the guards had a lookout all around. Inside that cone-shaped top up there, the monks put their church bell. It was not only rung for prayers, but also as a warning when the Danish raiders were in sight. And then everybody ran to the Round Tower. The monks brought their sacred vessels and precious things from the cathedral and the abbey, and the people from the villages came running with their belongings. They all climbed a long ladder to the doorway, up there. Twenty-six feet from the ground, the entrance is.

"When everybody was safely inside, the ladder was pulled up. When the Danes arrived, they were furious, because this time they couldn't plunder as before. And they couldn't capture the tower with their bows and arrows, nor with their swords. They could not even burn the tower, because it is all of stone."

"But what if the invaders made ladders and went up to the doorway too?" I ask.

"That was just too bad for them, because the people in the Round Tower would then pour hot water on their heads and shoot at them from the windows with bows and arrows!

"Not only here did they have a Round Tower. They were built all over the country. Seventy of them are still standing, after more than a thousand years. And many more were built at that time.

"And now, stroll around, all of you, and see for yourselves."

There are many crosses here. We find an old one with a little stone roof on top, and beautiful designs carved into the stone, flowers and ornaments. The letters of the inscription are almost worn away, but I can see the first letter clearly, it is an O. "That might be the burial cross of an O'Shaugnessy," explains Sister Carmel, "perhaps one of the descendants of King Guaire—they were O'Shaugnessys. And the ring around the cross we have only in Ireland. That's why it is called the Irish Cross."

I walk over to the ruined cathedral of Saint Colman and go into the big hall inside. I like exploring by myself. The walls are still standing, and ivy grows all over them. This must be the place where Saint Colman and the young monk had their dinner, and where the dishes came flying in. And there is the big window! I climb up to it.

I scratch my leg and fall back, but I try again. I put my hands up to the sill and pull myself up. From here I can see all over the place: the Round Tower and the crosses, and everybody walking around. I don't think I could jump down here on the outside wall. It is surely eight feet down to the ground.

"Padraic! Will you come down! And be quick!" This is Master Moylan calling me. I jump, and fall on my hands and knees.

"I did not mean you to jump down the wall, Padraic! You might have broken a leg!"

I really thought I was to jump right down when Master Moylan called me—stupid of me. And I say that I didn't mean it, and that I am very sorry indeed.

"Really, Padraic, these walls here are very old. They might tumble down if you tread on them, or great pieces might come loose!"

Master Moylan and Sister Carmel call us together, it is time for us to go back. We climb into the trucks and travel again over the Road of the Flying Dishes.

And then we start singing again. Master Moylan wants to hear "This Native Land of Mine," and we sing it:

> She is a rich and rare land,
> She's a fresh and fair land,
> She is a dear and rare land,
> This native land of mine.
>
> No men than hers are braver,
> Her women's hearts ne'er waver,
> I'd freely die to save her
> And think my lot divine.
>
> She's not a dull or cold land,
> No! She's a warm and bold land.
> O she's a true and old land,
> This native land of mine.

GLOSSARY

Bogland
The wet and soft ground where only heather grows. From this ground we cut the turf for fuel. One-seventh of all Ireland is bogland.

"Cead mile failté"
"A hundred thousand welcomes," an old Irish greeting.

Saint Colman
A saintly man who lived in our County Clare. He is the patron saint of our church, and he built the abbey of Kilmacduagh in the seventh century.

Carrageen moss
The reddish seaweed we collect on our shore. Mammy makes pudding from it.

Curragh
Shallow boats made of tarred canvas over wooden frames. They are very light and go very fast over the rough waves near the shore—but one needs a lot of experience to handle them. They turn over easily.

Dublin
The capital of our country.

Hurling
The game everybody plays in Ireland. We play it with a wooden stick and try to drive the small cork ball into the other team's goal.

Leprechauns
Those wee little fairy shoemakers who hide their gold treasures. I have never seen one.

Saint Patrick
The patron saint of our country, because he made the Irish a Christian people when he came to us in the year 432.

Periwinkles
Small black snails I find between the stones on our shore. I sell them for pocket money.

Poblacht na H'eireann
The Irish name for The Republic of Ireland.

Shamrock
A three-leaf clover. It grows in bunches all over Ireland, and it is our national emblem.

Shannon River
Our longest river, 250 miles long.

Turf
The fuel we use in our fireplaces, for cooking and baking. It is cut from the bogland and dried in chunks.

Valera
Eamon de Valera was a leader in the Irish rebellion of 1916, and he became the first Prime Minister of the independent Republic of Ireland.

Maps drawn by Anne Marie Jauss